# From Our Eyes

*Takeshi M. James*

# Human Eye

Human eye: specialized sense organ capable of receiving visual images, which are then carried to the brain.

Davson, Hugh and Perkins, Edward. Encyclopedia Britannica, 2 nd ed., "Human Eye". Encyclopedia Britannica, August 7, 2020. https://wwwbritannica.com/science/human-eye (accessed December 1, 2020).

# About the Author

Takeshi M. James was born and raised on the Southside of Chicago. She attended Chicago Public Schools (CPS) from kindergarten through high school. Takeshi attended Grambling State University for three years, returned home, and transferred to Chicago State University where she earned two Master degrees. Takeshi is now a passionate educator of 23 years, serving as a Principal within CPS. Takeshi values quality time with her family, is the single parent of one son and is truly grateful for her life's journey thus far!

# Dedication & Message

Takeshi dedicates this book to her only son, her family, students, parents, and educators all over the world. Takeshi desires for everyone who reads this book to be inspired by the power of his or her eyes because manifestation begins with a vision. As a mom and educator, Takeshi has very high expectations for students, educators, and parents alike. The overall message to her audience is to dream BIG and always believe in yourself, for you are a conqueror who can overcome any adversity!

# *Special Thanks*

Takeshi gives special thanks to Arielle Akines, her cousin Shanice, and Aunt Deb for helping her to extend her vision for this book more clearly.

*Teacher Ms. Simone:* Good morning class and welcome to the eighth grade. I hope you are all excited about being here today. I am your teacher, Ms. Simone. Before we begin class, I must tell you that I have one goal for this year. We are going to have a phenomenal year of teaching and learning!

*Ms. Simone:* Hey guys, I remember going to school on the first day and the teacher would always instruct us to write a paragraph about what we did over the summer. "Because that was sometimes a chore for me, I'm going to spare you the agony," she giggles.

*Several Students:* "Blurting, "oh thank you, thank you!", as they laughed with cheer.

*Ms. Simone:* Today, each of you will have an opportunity to respond to the question of the day which is, when someone looks into your eyes what do they see? I'm going to give you a few moments to think about that. Again think, when someone looks into your eyes what do they see? Now, there will be no formal grade, but, this will be a good way for us to get to know one another.

*Ms. Simone:* Let's get started, who's first? Tell me your name please!

Student: Leroy White.

*Ms. Simone:* Hello, Leroy White, nice to meet you. You look very eager to speak. Tell us, when someone looks into your eyes, what do they see?

*Leroy:* When someone looks in my eyes, I hope that they see the passion for animals that dwells within me. Ultimately it is my goal to become a veterinarian, "I just love caring for animals," he exclaimed. I have two dogs, a guinea pig, and a hamster at home. The best part of my day is when I am able to relax, take care of, and wind down with my animals. I often visualize the day when I can help people care for their animals.

*Ms. Simone:* "Oh my, that's awesome, we're just going to have to call you Mr. Vet from now on!"

*Leroy:* He chuckles, "thank you." I can hear it now, someone coming into my office crying, "it's my cat, my cat!" I need to see Veterinarian White please, it's an emergency!" and I'll be right there to help.

*Ms. Simone:* Mr. Vet, there's something about your passion that makes me believe that you will be an extraordinary veterinarian one day. And, yes, I can see the fire in your eyes! Would anyone else like to share?

*Ms. Simone:* Is it Xavier?

*Student:* Yes, it's Xavier Jamar.

*Ms. Simone:* Nice to meet you, Xavier Jamar. When someone looks into yours eyes, what do they see?

*Xavier:* He took a long deep breath and spoke, "when someone looks into my eyes, I believe that they see hunger and thirst."

*Ms. Simone:* She responded, "hmmm, what an unpredictable response Xavier!" I never expected to hear that. Can you tell us a bit more about the hunger and thirst in your eyes? Where did they come from?

*Xavier:* Well, as a young black male from the Southside of Chicago, and being raised by a single mother, it has been a different experience for me than other kids.  People see hunger because when I am faced with hard things.... adversity... I always push through, even through the of toughest times.

*Ms. Simone:* "Now, that's impressive!" You're really focused on achieving greatness.

*Xavier:* "Yeah, I guess I am!", he mutters and nods his head. You see, sometimes it saddened me to see my mom paying all the bills, attending parent conferences and my sporting events alone, while most other kids had both parents present. But, despite it all, she never complained, barely missed a game, held me accountable for my grades, and always smiled with grace. So, it's that passion and the love that she has for me that created the hunger and thirst that people see in my eyes. And believe it or not, it's not just in my eyes, that same hunger and thirst also resonates within my heart and soul. Today, I am happy to just be unapologetically me, Xavier Jamar, with hunger and thirst in my eyes.

"The ultimate measure of a man in not where he stands in moments of comfort and convenience, but where he stands at the times of challenge and controversy."

-Martin Luther King Jr.

*Ms. Simone:* "Wow, absolutely amazing." I didn't think that each of your responses would take up so much time, but I'm glad that we got to hear from both of you. We will be able to hear from a few more students after lunch and recess.

*Xavier:* Thanks, no one has ever asked a question like that before. I'd been holding these thoughts in for awhile, I appreciate this experience and I'll keep the power in my eyes ignited.

*Xavier:* Ms. Simone before we leave for lunch and recess can you tell the class what you see when you look into the eyes of your students?

*Ms. Simone:* She laughs, "you're on a roll for the first day of school. I don't think anyone else really wants to hear that."

*Several students screaming:* "Yes, come on Ms. Simone!" Please!!! Yes, we do!!! Please, we want to hear it!!!"

*Ms. Simone:* "Well, well, well Xavier, look at what you have started," she giggles.   We have about 8 minutes until lunch and recess.  "I'll give it a try," she declared, standing up tall.

*Ms. Simone:* When I look into the eyes of my students, I see promise. I see a sense of hope. I see leaders. I see risk-takers. I see fighters. I see fathers and mothers providing for, communicating with, and leading their families. I see friends and foes united. *I see POWER!!!* But, students, you know there's something that you may find a little odd... I also see me when I look into the eyes of my students!

"When you look into the eyes of others, it's not about the color of their skin, but the love that lives in their hearts... For we are all human beings, we just want to be loved."
- Kyle X. James

*Xavier:* That's funny, how do you see you when you look into our eyes?

*Ms. Simone:* She gestures and says, "hmmm, quite frankly, I'm glad you asked."

*Ms. Simone:* Well students, I'll tell you. Life for me ain't been no easy ride.

*Ms. Simone:* You see, when I was a little girl about your age, I had just transferred to a new school after attending five to six elementary schools. As if that wasn't bad enough, I was wearing a cast on my shoulder from being tackled while playing football.

*Ms. Simone:* So as you could imagine, I was teased by my classmates on my first days of entering that new school.  But, as the days went by, I began to create friendships and my grades began to soar. I completed elementary school, graduated from high school, attended college, earned two master's degrees and that's how I am able to stand in front of you today as your teacher.  Therefore, when I look into your eyes I see me because that same potential lies within you to accomplish any goal that you set for yourselves. Now, I'm not saying that the road will be easy, but you'll have a village cheering you on to help you make it to the finish line.  When I look at you, I see warriors who persevere through adversities.  *But, above all, when I look in your eyes I see GREATNESS, I mean, kind-hearted students who will work diligently to make a difference in the lives of others.*  So, as we head to lunch and recess, always remember that when you look into the eyes of another, always look for the good in them. Capture the vision and speak greatness unto them!  Oh boy, look at the time. We better get going before we're late. Have fun guys.

*Student Paige Elaina to Student Paisley Anne:* "It's fascinating how much I felt her heart when she was talking" -she smiled- "Ms. Simone's story was great!"

*Student Paisley Anne:* "Yeah, it was pretty cool, but deep though." I've never took any time to think about what people may see when they look in my eyes.

*Paige Elaina:* Girl, I've known you since the first grade. I see a nurse or a doctor when I look into your eyes. Every time we hang out, you're always so nice to others and if you ever see someone hurting, you always go and help. I like the way that you run to the rescue of others.  You are very nurturing. "From now on, I'm going to call you Dr. Paisley Anne," they both burst out laughing.

*Paisley Anne:* "Awww, thank you," she whispered.

*Student Javier:* Hey Marquis, I was just thinking, I'm planning on going to trade school after I finish high school. It's always been my dream to follow in my dad's footsteps.

*Student Marquis:* Yeah, your dad is one of the best bricklayers around.

*Javier:* Thanks, but, I was thinking more about you and what I see when I look in your eyes. Man, you're like the brother that I never had.

*Marquis:* I feel the same about you bro.

*Javier:* I look up to you. You are a natural born leader. I believe what Ms. Simone said about there being greatness in us. I see that a lot when I look at you. Think about it man, you've always earned straight A's, you're president of the debate team, captain of the basketball team and, you just love serving in the community. "Boy, you should run for class president.", he smirked.

*Marquis:* "Man, thank you!", he added. "You are something special yourself."

*Javier:* But, what about running for class president? Hey, forget class president, I'll vote for you to be the next President of the United States. "Man, can't you see it, you living in the White House and me, coming to visit?", he laughed aloud.

*Javier:* Laughing hysterically, "boy, you are hilarious!" I gotcha bro, but for now, let's just focus on class president. "I'll do it!" Can you help me with my campaign? Heck, you can just be my manager.

*Marquis:* "Indeed, I will!" They fist bump. "You're going to shine bright like a diamond my brother!" Keep that twinkle and sparkle of greatness in your eyes President Javier, you're going places!

*Javier:* "Man, you're the best!" he sighed, thanks.

"Anyone who claims to be a leader must speak like a leader. That means speaking with integrity and truth."
—Vice President Kamala Harris

*Ms. Simone:* Alright class, I hope that you had a great lunch and a little fun at recess. Let's continue with our question of the day. Who wants to go first?

*Student Bianca:* She raises her hand and says, "me!"

*Ms. Simone:* Now, tell me your name, you know I'm still learning names.

*Student Bianca:* It's Bianca Avery.

*Ms. Simone:* Look at you with all that enthusiasm...
It's nice to meet you, Bianca Avery.

*Bianca:* "Thank you, she mutters." May I tell you something?

*Ms. Simone:* Why sure!

*Bianca:* You know, I didn't play at recess. I was really thinking about how we haven't even been in school for a full day and we've already learned so much. You know, "something tells me that this is going to be a great year!"

*Ms. Simone:* "Yes, it is!"

*Bianca:* I'm excited to hear more, can we get back to discussing the power in our eyes?

*Ms. Simone:* Sounds like a plan! Please take your seats. Who'd like to go next?

*Reflection Assignment:*

Now that you have gotten to familiarize yourself with all of the characters, take some time to think about which character that you can relate to the most, and why. Then, in the space below, identify that character, explain why you selected that character, and make a personal connection to that character. Use information from the text and your own knowledge to formulate your response. Before you begin, visualize the character, his/her actions, and his/her traits so that you are able provide a valid description of your character and your personal connection to that character.

The character that I most identify with is _____

I selected this character because he/she _____

_____

_____

The reason that I connect to this character the most is because

_____

_____

_____

_____

_____

_____

_____

_____

*"Education teaches us compassion and kindness, connection to others."*
*–First Lady, Jill Biden*

*Homework:*

Please take a few minutes to think about when someone looks into your eyes, what will they see. Use the space below to construct your response. Remember, to use complete sentences to explain the greatness that dwells within you, try closing your eyes to get the vision before you begin writing. *You will not be required to share response!

_____

_____

_____

_____

_____

_____

_____

_____

_____

_____

_____

_____

_____

_____

_____

*"The only thing worse than being blind is having sight but no vision."*
*– Helen Keller*

Made in the USA
Monee, IL
09 September 2021